D0714561

GAZELLES
ELEPHAN
GIRAFFE
BATS
PARROTS
TORTOISE
PENGUINS
ZOO
WARTHOGS

There's trouble at the zoo today...

The animals have run away!

Find and follow the tortoise on every page!

1 very tall giraffe
Spot the little white mouse.

trying hard not to laugh.
Where is the ladybird?
Find 1 green bird.

2 elephants in socks

playing
peek-a-boo
in the
rocks.
Where is the hippo hiding?
Peek-a-boo!
Spot 3 green lizards.

3 orange gazelles jumping high –

Find my 4 froggy friends.

they don't need
trampolines to fly!
Spot the soaring dog — and his hat!
Spot 2 penguins doing backflips.

4 gibbons, long and slim,
Where is my second banana?
Who woke me up?

swinging by the jungle gym!
Spot the balancing lizard.
Who's in there?
Find the jumping mouse.

# 5 pretty pink flamingos

Spot the pink umbrella.

posing in the cake shop windows!

Find 4 slithering snakes.

6 zebras, white and black,
Spot the dog in a white hat.

crossing over the
road and back.
Spot 4 mice out and about.
Where's my other shoe?

7 batty little bats wearing silly party hats.
Find a boot out of place.
Spot 10 pink birds at the party.

Where is the little bumblebee?

8 penguins keeping cool
Where is my pink ball?

splashing at the swimming pool.
Spot 2 bunnies in swimming caps.

**9** sneaky little parrots
hiding by the piles of carrots.

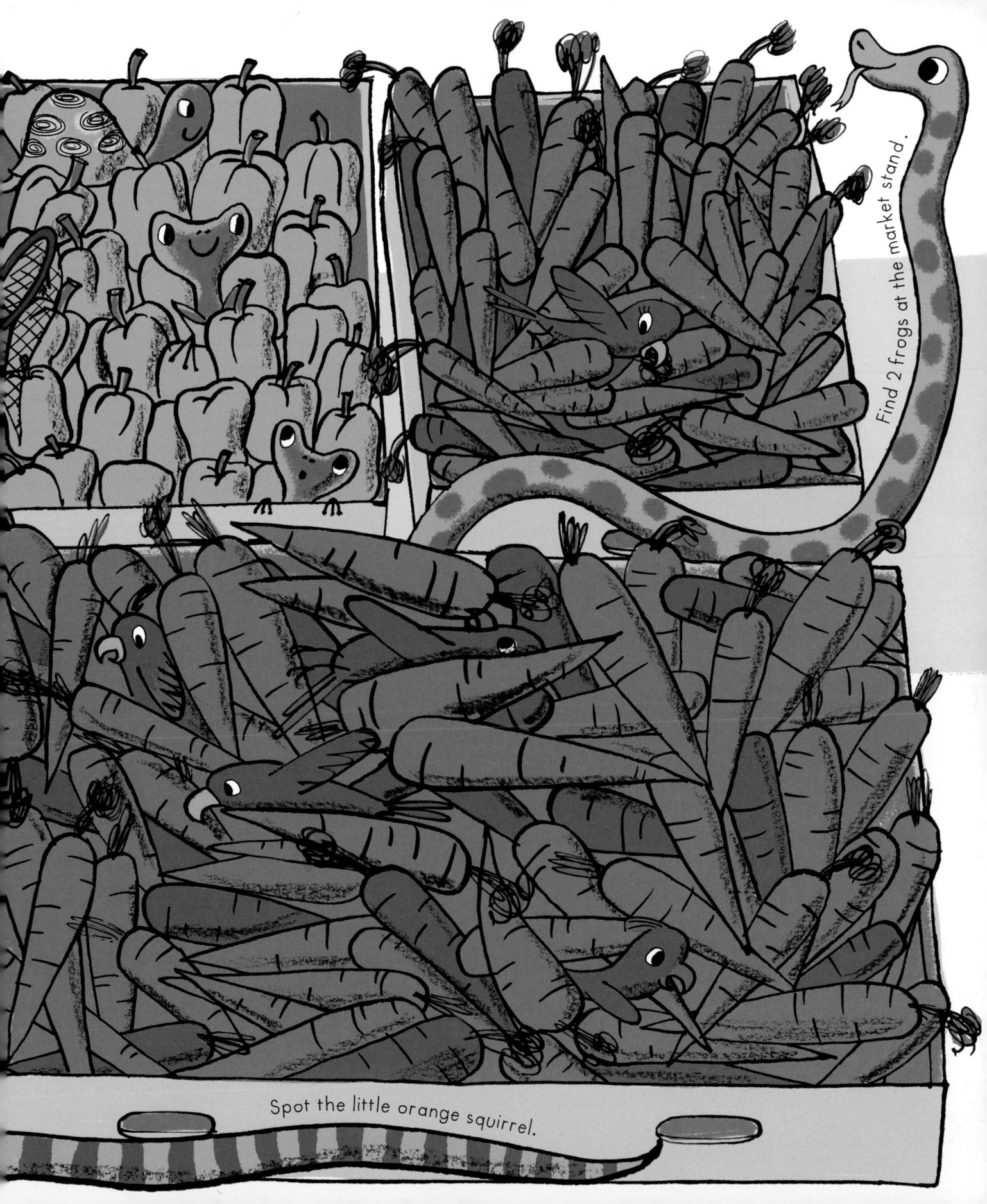
Find 2 frogs at the market stand.
Spot the little orange squirrel.

10 warthogs tapping feet
Spot the snoozing mouse.
Can you find my 2 bunny friends?

dancing to a hip-hop beat!
Find the fox in sunglasses.
here is my orange bag?

The keeper says,

"Let's have no fuss.
Now, everybody,
on the bus!"

Soon they're back
home in the zoo,

Spot the warthog who is still dancing!

but uh oh, Tortoise, where are you?

# THE END